Making a Mud Pie

by Carrie Waters
illustrated by Sue Williams

HOUGHTON MIFFLIN   BOSTON

Printed in India

ISBN-13: 978-0-547-01736-5
ISBN-10: 0-547-01736-7

3 4 5 6 7 8 9 0940 15 14 13 12 11 10

"I can make a mud pie,"
said Max.
"I can make a
mud pie, too,"
said Jenny.

"I will get some dirt,"
said Max.
He put some dirt
in his pail.

"I can get some dirt, too,"
said Jenny.
She put dirt in her pail.

"Now I will get
some water," said Max.
He put water in his pail.

Jenny put water
in her pail, too.

"Look!
I made a lot of mud!"
Max said.

He put his mud
in a pie pan.
Jenny put her mud
in a pan, too.

"Look!" said Jenny.
"You made a mud pie."

"But **I** made a worm pie!"

Responding

TARGET SKILL **Text and Graphic Features** Pick two pictures. Tell how the words go with the pictures. Make a chart.

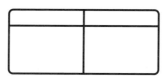

Write About It

Text to World Why is dirt important for growing things? Write a list of facts about dirt that you could put in a report.

all	**no**
good	**play**
he	**said**
make	**she**

LEARN MORE WORDS

dirt	**worm**

✔ **TARGET SKILL** **Text and Graphic Features** Tell how words work with art.

✔ **TARGET STRATEGY** **Summarize** Stop to tell important events as you read.

GENRE **Realistic fiction** is a story that could happen in real life.